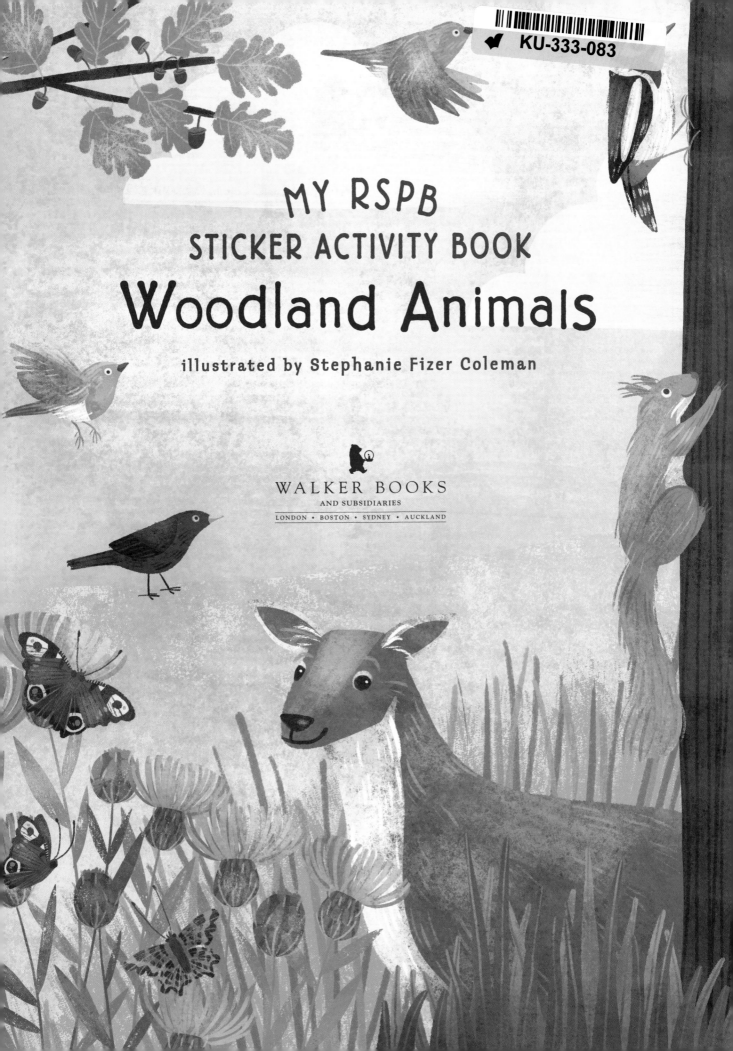

MY RSPB
STICKER ACTIVITY BOOK
Woodland Animals

illustrated by Stephanie Fizer Coleman

WALKER BOOKS
AND SUBSIDIARIES
LONDON · BOSTON · SYDNEY · AUCKLAND

ANIMAL HOMES

At the edge of the woods, animals are snuggled
up in their homes. Can you join the dots to
reveal who lives where? Colour them in and
add your baby animal stickers to their homes.

A bluebell can take about five years to grow from a seed into a flower.

Squirrels build nests called 'dreys'. They are made from leaves, moss and twigs.

Fox cubs live entirely on their mother's milk until they are four weeks old.

BEAUTIFUL BUTTERFLIES

These fluttering butterflies are visiting flowers to find food.
Can you finish their wings by copying the patterns and
colouring them in? Then try designing your very own butterfly!

Butterflies have long tubes on their heads,
which they use to sip nectar from flowers.

The red admiral butterfly lays its eggs on nettles.

The peacock butterfly has a spot that looks like an eye on each wing, to scare predators.

IN THE TREETOPS

Up in the trees, birds build nests with twigs, feathers and moss so they can lay their eggs. Use your stickers to help build this siskin's nest and to finish the squirrel puzzle, then colour in the bird.

Once the siskin's eggs have hatched, the parents will feed their chicks for about two weeks until they are old enough to leave the nest.

UP IN THE SKY

The forest is full of birds swooping and soaring!
Can you find the matching pairs and spot the odd one out?
Add more birds to the trees and branches using your stickers.

The chiffchaff gets its name from the sound of its song.

Like squirrels, jays gather acorns in the autumn and store them to eat later.

ANIMAL HOMES

BABY SQUIRRELS

FOX CUBS

BULLFINCH CHICKS

RABBIT KITTENS

BEAUTIFUL BUTTERFLIES

COMMON BLUE

ORANGE TIP

COMMA

SPECKLED WOOD

IN THE TREETOPS

SISKIN

SQUIRREL PUZZLE

EXTRA STICKERS

UP IN THE SKY

WOODPECKER – MALE

WOODPECKER – FEMALE

GREAT TIT

COAL TIT

WREN

THRUSH

NIGHT-TIME

PIPISTRELLE BAT

HEDGEHOG

RABBIT

BANK VOLE

CREEPY CRAWLIES

BEETLE

LADYBIRD

SNAIL

BEE

GRASSHOPPER

SPIDER

AT THE RIVERBANK

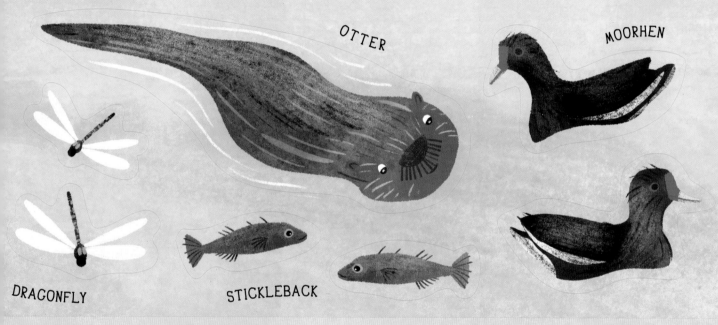

OTTER

MOORHEN

DRAGONFLY

STICKLEBACK

EXTRA STICKERS

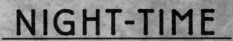

NIGHT-TIME

In the dark night, lots of animals are stirring among the trees... Where are these ones hiding?

Fox   Badger   Tawny Owl

Moth   Toad   Weasel

Now add more night-time animals using your stickers!

Animals that are mostly awake at night are known as 'nocturnal'.

CREEPY CRAWLIES

A colony of ants has built a nest underground, but one ant has got lost. Can you help her find the way to the queen ant? Colour in the flowers and creatures above ground and add some creepy-crawly stickers.

Worms help plants to grow by pulling dead leaves down into the soil to make nutrients, which is 'plant food'.

START

Wood mice like to eat insects and worms as well as seeds and berries.

FINISH

Ants are so strong they can lift objects twenty times heavier than themselves!

AT THE RIVERBANK

Can you join the dots to reveal who is having
a refreshing drink at the edge of the river?
Then finish the picture with colour and use
your stickers to add more water-loving animals.

Kingfishers fly low over water to hunt for fish and insects.

Moorhens build their nests among plants in the water.

Frogs don't need to drink water to survive — they allow it to soak through their skin instead.

ON THE FOREST FLOOR

Watch where you step! The forest floor is alive with activity.
Can you spot 6 differences between these two pictures?